# Humphrey Lyttelton's Jazz and Big Band Quiz

Which jazz musicians were known as:
—Cootie?
—Hootie?
—Bootie?
—Tootie?
—Zutty?
—Cutty?

Who said Billie Holiday: 'She sang as if her shoes were too tight'?

Or of the Beatles: 'It's just children's music'?

Who went by the title of:
—Mr B?
—Lady Day?
—The King of Swing?
—The President?
—The Sentimental Gentleman of Swing?

Who died:
—in an air raid?
—at the dentist?
—in a plane crash?
—in a street fight?

Whose nicknames were:
—Cat?
—Bird?
—Hawk?
—Pony?
—Mule?

These are a few of the questions in this quiz for jazz and big band fans. They range from the easy to the impossible, and they are all diverting. Many of them are based on a series of old photographs which are as entertaining and unexpected as the questions.

Humphrey Lyttelton, himself a distinguished band-leader and trumpeter, is famous also as the presenter of a jazz record programme.
*The cover picture of Humphrey Lyttelton is from a colour transparency by courtesy of David Redfern Photography.*

# Humphrey Lyttelton's

# Jazz and Big Band Quiz

B.T. BATSFORD LTD · LONDON

First published 1979
© Humphtey Lyttelton 1979
Designed by
Alan Hamp
Filmset in 'Monophoto' Melior by
Servis Filmsetting Ltd, Manchester

Printed in Great Britain by
The Anchor Press Ltd
Tiptree, Essex,
for the publishers B.T. Batsford Ltd
4 Fitzhardinge Street, London W1H 0AH

ISBN 0 7134 2011 1

# Contents

Acknowledgment  6

Introduction  7

Quiz One          Bandleaders and their Instruments  9
Quiz Two          Musicians' Titles  13
Quiz Three        Musicians and their Nicknames  14
Quiz Four         Bands, Past and Present  15
Quiz Five         Dramatic Deaths  21
Quiz Six          Singers and their Bands  22
Quiz Seven        Tunes and their Composers  25
Quiz Eight        Jazz Partnerships  26
Quiz Nine         Spot the Errors  30
Quiz Ten          Familiar Faces – Strange Names  32
Quiz Eleven       Books and Authors  36
Quiz Twelve       Family Likenesses  37
Quiz Thirteen     A Mixed Bag  41
Quiz Fourteen     Nicknames and Real Names  43
Quiz Fifteen      Biographies  47
Quiz Sixteen      Married Couples  49
Quiz Seventeen    'Scrambled' Bands  52
Quiz Eighteen     Vocal Groups  53
Quiz Nineteen     Descriptions of Recordings  57
Quiz Twenty       More Family Likenesses  59
Quiz Twenty-one   Praise from Fellow Musicians  62
Quiz Twenty-two   Faces and Names  64
Quiz Twenty-three The Story behind the Tune  68
Quiz Twenty-four  Tell-Tale Details  70
Quiz Twenty-five  Countries of Birth  73
Quiz Twenty-six   Unflattering Remarks  74
Quiz Twenty-seven Unusual Jazz Instruments  76
Quiz Twenty-eight True or False?  79
Quiz Twenty-nine  Zoological Nicknames  83

Answers  85

# Acknowledgment

The author and publishers would like to thank the following individuals
and organizations for the use of the various photographs and stills
appearing in this book:

Associated Press Ltd
John and Theresa Chilton
Camera Press Ltd
Decca Record Co Ltd
EMI Music Publishing Ltd
Flair Photography
Ronald Grant Archive
*Jazz Journal International*
Jazz Music Books
Keystone Press Agency Ltd
John E. Kuhlman
London Features International Ltd
MGM Pictures
National Film Archive
Pablo Records
Popperfoto
David Redfern Photography
*Time Out*
Twentieth Century-Fox Co Ltd
Universal Pictures
Verve Records
Valerie Wilmer
World Jazz Records

While the publishers have made every effort to obtain permission from the
copyright holders of the illustrations in this book, they would be most
grateful to learn of any inadvertent omissions from the list of
acknowledgments.

# Introduction

A few years ago I contributed some questions on jazz to the television quiz 'Mastermind'. The contestant, who had already gone through two chosen subjects on his way to the semi-final, confessed to me, when I met him some months later backstage at a concert, that he had been rather too free with the hospitality before the programme, to the extent that he very nearly failed on the very first question of all, which was 'What is your chosen subject?' Even so, I was somewhat embarrassed by the number of questions on which he 'passed'. I had believed that most of them were quite easy!

The fact, which this experience brought home to me, is that there is a relatively small number of people who are what the Americans call 'jazz buffs'. They read all the magazines, devour the information on the back of long-playing records, fill notebooks with cuttings, photographs and odd bits of information, and listen to jazz programmes on the radio as keenly as ambitious students at a lecture. There is a far larger body of people who go to concerts, buy records and generally enjoy jazz as and where they find it, without really bothering to take in much information about its history and personalities.

Both groups of people would probably be drawn into having a go at a quiz such as this. But the problem of formulating questions which would give the latter group a chance while at the same time taxing the expertise of the former is enormous. For this reason, I have taken jazz *and* big bands as my brief, bringing in also some popular vocalists whose links with jazz will certainly be deemed tenuous by the dedicated jazz buffs. I have also decided against dividing the quiz into sections of increasing hardness. It seemed to me that everyone would have more fun if each set of questions contained hard and simple elements. So be not downhearted if you can only give three or four correct answers in each set – you might still amass quite a respectable score by the end. The alert contestant with a retentive memory will be able to pick up some clues along the way, and I have included quite a few visual questions which are open to guesswork by someone with no knowledge of the subject at all.

Many of the questions come from the common stock of jazz lore and information, to which an heroic regiment of biographers, discographers, archivists and commentators have contributed over the years. All the facts have been checked to the best of my ability from a variety of sources. They are too numerous and diverse to acknowledge in detail, so I offer thanks for them all. But there are some specific works which have been at my elbow throughout, feeding me with ideas and facts. They are Leonard Feather's *Encyclopedia of Jazz* (Horizon Press), and the separate Encyclopedias of *Jazz in the Sixties* and *the Seventies*, by the same author (Quartet Books), John Chilton's *Who's Who of Jazz* (Chilton Book Company), the *Guiness Book of Music Facts and Feats*, whose section on jazz was contributed by Brian Rust (Guiness Superlatives Ltd.), *Tell Your Story* by Eric Townley (Storyville Publications), and *Hear Me Talkin' To Ya*, that invaluable compendium of jazz musicians' 'quotes' compiled by Nat Shapiro and Nat Hentoff (Penguin Books). My effusive thanks must go, too, to the suppliers of all the photographs – acknowledged separately elsewhere – and to Annette Brown, who went beyond the basic requirements of my quiz to track down and amass a collection of pictures that make up an attractive and informative pictorial album in their own right.

In the whole quiz, there are 430 marks for the taking. If you score over 400 I offer congratulations tempered only by the fear that the pedantic postcard that I receive whenever I make a slip on my BBC Radio 'Best of Jazz' programme may well emanate from you. A score of between 250 and 400 entitles you to call yourself a Jazz Buff, though I wouldn't do it in the hearing of anyone who cares for the dignity of the English language. If you get between 100 and 250 marks, it suggests that you are good at quizzes but not too hot on jazz – or *vice versa*. Anything less than 100 earns my deep respect. Anyone who can slog through to the end with such little encouragement must be a good sport. So get to it – you have nothing to lose!

*For the answers please turn to the end of the book*

# One

## Bandleaders and their Instruments

Identify the following bandleaders from their pictures below, and then from the accompanying list pick the instrument which the bandleader played. (One mark for each identification, and an extra mark if you get the instrument right. Maximum, 20 marks)

| | |
|---|---|
| Trumpet | Trombone |
| Trombone | Piano |
| Piano | Clarinet |
| Clarinet | Vibraphone |
| Drums | Drums |

1

2

3

4

5

6

7

8

**9**

**10**

# Two

## Musicians' Titles

Titles have been scattered among jazz musicians with all the profligacy of a New Year's Honours List. Here are a few of them, to which you have to put a name. (One mark each. Maximum 10 marks)

1 Father of the Blues.

2 The Boss of the Blues.

3 The President, or Pres.

4 The High Priest of Bop.

5 Lady Day.

6 Mr Five by Five.

7 The King of Swing.

8 The Sentimental Gentleman of Swing.

9 The Hi-de-Ho Man.

10 Mr B.

# Three

## Musicians and their Nicknames

Jazz abounds in weird and colourful nicknames. Sometimes the musician is best known by the nickname, in other instances the nickname is reserved for close associates or inveterate name-droppers. Identify the following with a full name or surname only. (One mark each. Maximum, 10 marks)

1 Cootie

2 Hootie

3 Bootie

4 Tootie

5 Zutty

6 Cutty

7 Zoot

8 Boots

9 Foots

10 Toots

# four

## Bands, Past & Present

Pictured below are ten long-established bands, past and present. It might help you to know that all of them are, or were, known by a corporate name, not by the name of the leader. (One mark each. Maximum, 10 marks)

1

2

3

**5**

**6**

7

8

**9**

**10**

20

# Five

## Dramatic Deaths

Jazz and popular music have had their share of spectacular and dramatic deaths. Here is a list of circumstances and dates, to which you have to put a name. (One mark each. Maximum 10 marks)

**WHO?**

1 Died of a seizure in a friend's apartment while laughing at a juggling act on TV. The date, 12 March 1955.

2 Died of pneumonia aboard the Santa Fé Chief en route from Los Angeles to New York. The date, 15 December 1943.

3 Is assumed to have died in a plane that disappeared over the English Channel en route from an English airfield to Paris. The date, 16 December 1944.

4 Died in a car accident on Route 61 between Memphis and Clarksdale, an event which, years later, provided the title for a play by American playwright, Edward Albee. The date, 26 September 1937.

5 Choked to death in his sleep exactly one week after his fifty-first birthday, probably as a result of taking sleeping pills after a heavy meal. The date, 26 November 1956.

6 Was accidentally shot dead during a fight in a dance hall in Orleans Street, Chicago, where he was playing piano. The date, 14 March 1929.

7 Was killed in a German air-raid while leading his band at the Café de Paris in London. The date, 8 March 1941.

8 Died in a fatal car accident while a passenger in the car of his bandleader at the time, cornetist Wild Bill Davison. The date, 1 March 1932.

9 Collapsed and died of a heart-attack while on a visit to his dentist. The date, 11 May 1970.

10 Died of cold and exposure on his own Harlem doorstep, having been unable to get into his house. The date, 29 February 1936.

# Six

## Singers and their Bands

Name the singer, and then choose from the list below the band with which he or she was associated in the early days. (One mark for naming the singer, a second for picking the right band. Maximum score, 20 marks)

| | |
|---|---|
| Les Brown | Tommy Dorsey |
| Earl Hines | Count Basie |
| Chick Webb | Charlie Barnet |
| Gene Krupa | Earl Hines |
| Benny Goodman | Paul Whiteman |

1

2

**3**

**4**

**5**

**6**

7

8

9

10

24

# Seven

## Tunes and their Composers

Here are some well known jazz 'standards' that have proved perennial favourites. But do you know who wrote them? (One mark each. Maximum, 10 marks. Where two names are involved, take a mark for naming just one of them)

1 'South Rampart Street Parade'

2 'King Porter Stomp'

3 'How High the Moon'

4 'Perdido'

5 'Carolina Shout'

6 'After You've Gone'

7 'Moanin'

8 'The Preacher'

9 'Darktown Strutter's Ball'

10 'Bill Bailey, Won't you Please Come Home'

# Eight

## Jazz Partnerships

The pictures below are grouped in pairs, each pair representing a famous or historic musical partnership. Identify the faces, and name the group or partnership in which they appeared. (One mark for each face identified and an extra mark for naming the group or partnership. Maximum, 15 marks)

2

3

5

# Nine

## Spot the Errors

Here are five paragraphs about musicians or pieces of music which are riddled with deliberate errors. At the end of each paragraph you are told how many errors you should have found. If you find any more than that, by all means award yourself extra marks, but keep it to yourself! (Maximum, 30 marks)

1 Scott Joplin, the famous New Orleans ragtime composer and uncle of the ill-starred pop singer Janis Joplin, is probably best known today for the piece called 'The Entertainer' which was part of Joplin's film score for the Peter Fonda–Robert Redford movie *The Sting*. But he wrote many varied works including a folk opera, 'Treemonisha' and the military march 'Blaze Away'. (5 errors)

2 The composition 'Tiger Rag', attributed to Nick La Rocca, the pianist and leader of the Original Dixieland Jazz Band, was the very first tune recorded by that band in its historic 1917 recording sessions. Over the years it has proved a favourite vehicle for jazz musicians. Tommy Dorsey's trumpet version of 1935 stands out, as do interpretations by Louis Armstrong's Hot Five and Duke Ellington. But some jazz pundits assert that the original ODJB version, with its now-familiar chant 'Hold That Tiger!', has never been surpassed. (5 errors)

3 Jazz talent seems to run in families. One has only to think of the Jones family that has produced pianist Hank, trumpeter Elvin and drummer Thad; the Smith family that can claim no less than four renowned blues singers – Mamie, Clara, Trixie and the incomparable Bessie, rightly called 'The Queen of the Blues'; the Teagarden family from California that produced one of the greatest jazz saxophonists, Jack Teagarden, as well as trumpeter Charlie, drummer Clois and pianist Norma; and the McPartlands – Jimmy, Marian and Dick – who have shone on cornet, piano and guitar respectively. (7 errors)

4 When Joe Turner recorded a blues called 'Ev'ry Day I Have The Blues' with Count Basie in 1955, few fans would have predicted that it would turn out to be one of Bob Basie's biggest hits. Fewer still would have known that the tune's composer, Peter Chatman, is a fine blues singer himself, known under the pseudonym 'Sunnyland Slim'. It may well have been the Neil Hefti arrangement that gave the straightforward 12-bar blues its popular boost. (5 errors)

5 Glenn Miller's composition 'In the Mood', famous as the signature-tune of the Glenn Miller Orchestra, introduced for the first time a catchy twelve-bar theme which has subsequently been copied in several other jazz pieces – eg. Wingie Manone's 'Tar Paper Stomp' and 'Jumpy Nerves' and Fletcher Henderson's 'Hot and Anxious'. The original Miller recording was distinguished by a melodic cornet solo by Bobby Hackett which has since remained an integral part of the arrangement. 'In the Mood' was featured in the Glenn Miller film biography *The Five Pennies* and is, of course, often played by British bands – Elliot Lawrence, Acker Bilk – who specialize in the Miller style, with its distinctive sound of trombone blended with saxophones. (8 errors)

# Ten

## Familiar Faces — Strange Names

Here are some quite familiar faces — and some unfamiliar names. They are the real names of the artists in the photographs, and you have to match them up. (One mark for identifying the face, an extra mark for getting the right name. Maximum 20 marks)

Salvatore Massaro                Ferdinand Joseph La Menthe

Arthur Arshawsky                 Ruth Jones

Lester Polfus                    Anthony Dominick Benedetto

Annabelle Short                  Eleanora McKay (a married name)

Clive Powell                     McKinley Morganfield

1

2

3

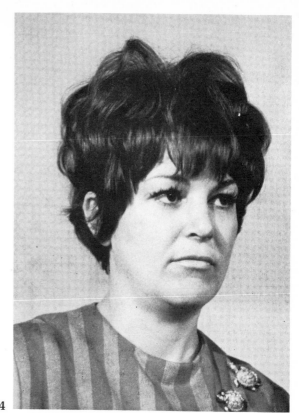

4

5

6

9

10

# Eleven

## Books and Authors

In the years since World War II, there has been a spate of books by, and about, famous jazz musicians. All those listed below are autobiographies. In each case, give the name of the author. (One mark each. Maximum 10 marks)

1 *Beneath the Underdog*

2 *Lady Sings The Blues*

3 *The Trouble with Cinderella*

4 *Owning Up*

5 *Music is my Mistress*

6 *We Called it Music*

7 *I Play as I Please*

8 *Treat it Gentle*

9 *Music on my Mind*

10 *Really the Blues*

# Twelve

## Family Likenesses

Here are some family likenesses for you to identify. Don't be deterred if some of the faces are new to you – there is room here for some inspired guesswork. Among the pictures below are three sets of brothers, one set of father-and-daughter and one set of father-and-son. (One mark for each face you identify, an extra mark for completing the pair. Maximum, 15 marks)

1

2

3

4

5

6

7

8

9

**10**

# Thirteen

## A Mixed Bag

Here's a chocolate box of assorted questions, some hard, some soft-centred, some concealing a surprise filling. (One mark per correct answer. Maximum 50 marks)

1  Which famous bandleader was once married to Betty Grable?
2  Who wrote a jazz suite based on Dylan Thomas's *Under Milk Wood*?
3  How old was Louis Armstrong when he died?
4  Who wrote 'St Louis Blues'?
5  Whose band had a composition written for it by Igor Stravinsky?
6  Which bandleader, saxophonist and composer is a Commander of the British Empire.
7  Which jazz clarinettist recorded with the Budapest String Quartet?
8  What have Maynard Ferguson, Oscar Peterson and Gil Evans in common?
9  When did a jazz band first record 'When the Saints Go Marching In'?
10  Which well-known American comedian played jazz piano and once led a band called the Original New Orleans Jazz Band?
11  Who wrote 'Basin Street Blues'?
12  Who was Andreamenentania Paul Razafinkeriefo?
13  Who is alleged to have said, and to whom, 'This one's for you, Rex!'?
14  Which has the greatest length of tubing, a trumpet or a cornet?
15  Which ragtime and jazz pianist was born in Baltimore in 1883 and is still alive and active at the time of writing?
16  Who hit the headlines in 1939 by abandoning his highly successful band and fleeing to Mexico?
17  What is a 'riff'?
18  Who wrote the tune 'Doctor Jazz'?
19  On which record was Lionel Hampton first heard soloing on vibraphone?
20  Clark Burroughs, Bob Morse, Gene Puerling, Don Shelton – what do these names represent?
21  Whose given names were William Henry Joseph Berthol Bonaparte Bertholoff?
22  To what family of instruments does the Mellophone belong?
23  In what jazz work does Madam Zajj appear?
24  Which jazz clarinettist composed the sentimental waltz hit, 'Little Sir Echo'?
25  Who was Blind Willie Dunn?
26  Which band was billed as 'The Biggest Little Band in America'?
27  For what service to jazz fans was Charles Delaunay responsible?
28  Who was Richard Bowden Jones?

29 With what occupations would you collectively associate Bing Crosby, Jack Teagarden and Mary Martin?

30 Who wrote a jazz 'suite' called 'Summer Sequence'?

31 Who wrote the music for a show called *Connie's Hot Chocolates* in 1929.

32 What was a Valide?

33 Three great jazz personalities – Sidney Bechet, Lester Young and Billie Holiday – died in the same year. Which year?

34 Who uttered the dictum 'Jazz must be played sweet, soft, plenty rhythm'?

35 Lennie Tristano, Art Tatum, Bud Powell, George Shearing – name the odd one out.

36 Which band did Louis Armstrong frequently cite as his favourite?

37 Who wrote a work called 'The Black Saint and The Sinner Lady'?

38 Who is 'The Kid from Red Bank'?

39 Cup, Harmon, straight, plunger – what do these words denote?

40 Who had a hit with a jazz version of 'Isle of Capri'?

41 What do the initials J.A.T.P. stand for?

42 Whom did Hollywood dub 'The King of Jazz' in 1930?

43 Who wrote the tune, 'Petite Fleur'?

44 Name the founder members of the Modern Jazz Quartet.

45 Who composed the blues song 'How Long, How Long', otherwise known as 'How Long Blues'?

46 'Stompin' at the Savoy' is a well-known jazz standard. What was the Savoy?

47 Which legendary jazz musician was born in Davenport, Iowa?

48 Who contributed the jazz score for the British film *Alfie*?

49 What is, or was, a 'goofus'?

50 What, outside of music, have Artie Shaw, Mickey Rooney and Frank Sinatra in common?

# Fourteen

## Nicknames and Real Names

Pictured below are ten musicians with familiar nicknames. You have to pick their *real* first names from the accompanying list. (10 marks)

1 Dizzy Gillespie
2 Pee Wee Russell
3 Bix Beiderbecke
4 Count Basie
5 Fats Domino
6 Buck Clayton
7 Cannonball Adderley
8 Cootie Williams
9 Acker Bilk
10 Muggsy Spanier

Leon
Bernard
John Birks
Antoine
William
Charles Ellsworth
Charles Melvin
Wilbur
Francis
Julian

2

3

4

5

**6**

**7**

**8**

9

10

# Fifteen

## Biographies

Here are some potted biographies from the jazz and big band world.
Identify the subjects. (One mark each. Maximum 10 marks)

1  This young Texas-born guitarist, playing in an obscure band, was brought
   to the attention of Benny Goodman, who signed him up when he was still
   only 23 years old. In less than two years he contracted tuberculosis and
   died at 26. But in those 21 months with Goodman, working mainly in the
   Benny Goodman Sextet, he carved himself a permanent niche in jazz
   history.

2  Although active in and around New Orleans during the first three decades
   of the century, this trumpet player did not come to the attention of jazz
   enthusiasts until 1942, when he made his first recordings. In a burst of
   publicity and recording activity, he became a figurehead of the New
   Orleans Revival, causing great excitement and controversy when he took a
   band of New Orleans men into the Stuyvesant Casino in New York in
   September 1945. His Indian summer was brief – he died in 1949 at his
   home in New Iberia.

3  Born in Pittsburgh in 1921, he taught himself piano at an early age,
   though he never learned to read music. Moved to New York in 1944 and
   was soon recording prolifically, with his own trio and also with such
   musicians as Charlie Parker and Wardell Gray. For most of his career,
   until his death in 1977, he toured in concert with a trio, earning wide
   popularity with a highly individual style of which a delayed, lagging beat
   in the right hand was a hallmark.

4  This son of a wealthy New York family was a student at Yale University
   when he began to gravitate towards jazz as a profession. At first he wrote
   jazz articles for such British publications as *Melody Maker* and
   *Gramophone*. But it is as a recording company executive with a flair for
   discovering talent (Billie Holiday, Count Basie's Band, Lionel Hampton,
   Aretha Franklin, Bob Dylan) that he is best known. A lifelong friend and
   adviser to Benny Goodman, whom his sister eventually married.

5  Born in London in 1927, this tenor-saxophone player worked in the bands
   of Ted Heath and Jack Parnell in his early days. Made his first visit to
   America as a member of the ship's band on the *Queen Mary*. Having
   established a reputation as a musician, largely as founder-member of a

band called the Jazz Couriers, he opened a jazz night-club in London in 1959 which has become one of the best known jazz-spots in the world.

**6** This alto-saxophone player, composer and arranger played with, and arranged for, many famous bands – Don Redman, Cab Calloway, Hot Lips Page, Lionel Hampton – before springing to worldwide fame in 1945 with his own band. His brash and extrovert versions of such tunes as 'Temptation', 'Flamingo' and 'You Go To My Head' shocked many jazz fans but brought him great success with rhythm 'n blues audiences. He died of a heart attack in 1965.

**7** Born in London in 1934, this child-prodigy was playing drums publicly at the age of seven. He was ten years old when he appeared as a guest with Glen Miller's AEF band, was subsequently billed as 'The Kid Krupa'. Went to America in 1955, toured with Woody Herman's Band on vibes. Has lived in America ever since, in constant demand for studio and recording work on both vibes and piano.

**8** This New Orleans-born trumpet-player became well-known in the Thirties, playing and singing in the Louis Armstrong style with a band called his New Orleans Gang. Having switched to a large dance-band through the Forties, he returned to small-band work in the latter years, achieving enormous success as a double-act with his wife, Keely Smith, backed by a booting rhythm 'n' blues-style band. He died in 1978.

**9** Born in California in 1920, this pianist and composer studied in his early years under Darius Milhaud and Arnold Schoenberg. He formed an experimental octet in 1946, a trio in 1949 and then, in 1951, brought together a quartet that lasted, with little change, until 1967. The critics often expressed reservations about his music, the public clearly did not. In recent years he has performed concerts with a quartet involving his three sons.

**10** This renowned New Orleans trumpet player was one of the first to earn the title of 'King'. Around 1912, he left New Orleans to tour America at the head of the Original Creole Orchestra, which visited Chicago and New York in 1915. Can be heard on old recordings by Doc Cook's Dreamland Orchestra and his own Jazz Cardinals. Legend has it that he turned down an offer to record in New York, leaving the way open for the Original Dixieland Jazz Band. He died in obscurity in 1933.

# Sixteen

## Married Couples

In the following pictures are five married couples, past or present – but all ten people shown have been well-known musicians or entertainers in their own right. Name them. (One mark each, maximum 10 marks)

1

2

3

4

5

# Seventeen

## 'Scrambled' Bands

In the following list, famous bands and their leaders have been shuffled around. Put them together correctly. (10 marks)

1 Fats Waller and his Red Hot Peppers

2 Les Brown and his Clouds of Joy

3 Nat Gonella's Hot Five

4 Louis Jordan's Royal Canadians

5 Guy Lombardo's Creole Jazz Band

6 Jelly Roll Morton's Band of Renown

7 Louis Armstrong and his Five Pennies

8 Andy Kirk and his Georgians

9 King Oliver's Tympani Five

10 Red Nichols and his Rhythm

# Eighteen

## Vocal Groups

A chance to pick up some easy marks here, with the straight identification of some famous vocal groups through the ages. (One mark for each identification. Maximum 10 marks)

1

4

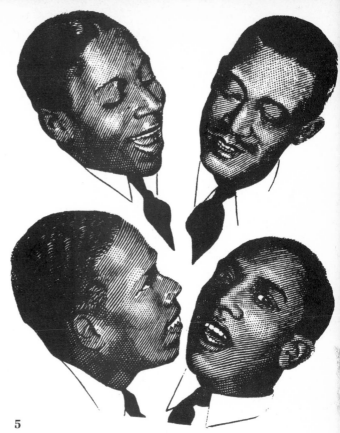

5

6

7

**8**

**9**

**10**

# Nineteen

## Descriptions of Recordings

As the presenter of a jazz record programme, I often receive letters describing, in incomplete and garbled terms, a piece that I have played and asking for the details. Can you name the well-known recordings from the following descriptions. One mark for the title, one for naming the band that recorded it. (Maximum, 10 marks)

**1** It begins with a solo bit on trumpet, out-of-tempo, which descends from a high note, climbs back up to an even higher one and then cascades down to a long low-note. Then the band comes in, with the trumpet playing the tune – I think it's a twelve-bar blues. After that, there's a simple sort of solo on trombone, and then a bit where the clarinet plays a phrase and the singer answers it. I think they do the last phrase together. Then there's a rather showy piano solo, in which the player sometimes seems to be imitating a trumpet sound by playing octaves. After that the trumpet comes in again with a long high note and a lot of very passionate phrases – but after another piano bit, it all ends very calmly.

**2** It's a long piece – goes on about six minutes, and it's by a big band. It starts with a sort of jungle rhythm on the tom-toms, over which the band comes in with a fierce-sounding introduction. Then it breaks into normal tempo with a swingy theme in a minor key that sounds as if it could be a popular song. This is followed by a clarinet solo, some more tom-toms and then a new theme that sounds slightly familiar to me, in which trombones and saxes in unison play a bass theme over which the trumpets come in with a snarling counter-melody. Then the band and drummer alternate, with the tom-toms playing more complicated rhythms each time. When the drummer brings the band in with a few beats on the cowbell, it sounds as if it's the end of the piece, but it starts up again with a breathy saxophone solo, a really discordant but exciting piece from the whole band, a wild trumpet bit and then a duet by clarinet and drums that gradually fades to a whisper. It ends like the first half, with some cowbell beats and a rousing last chorus in which the drummer really sounds as if he's enjoying himself.

**3** It's a New Orleansish sort of band, with what sounds like a tuba rather than a string bass. They go straight into an opening tune in which the trumpet leads very forcefully and there's plenty of strong clarinet, too. Then there's a bit which the trumpeter plays solo. It sounds like a sort of verse, but I notice that he plays the phrases differently each time –

to give it variation, I suppose. The clarinet solos next with a very strident sound and a distinct shake or wobble in the long notes – a highly individual style, I would say. After that, there are a few chords on the banjo, and then the trumpet-player plays a fantastic solo almost entirely on his own, with the band just playing a chord here and there. When the trumpet leads out of this into the final chorus, it's very wild and exciting.

4  It sounds a very sad sort of song, about being poor and having no friends. The singer has quite a low voice for a woman, but it's very strong and powerful. She sings a verse and chorus with what sounds like a very small band playing in the background. Then there's a solo on trumpet or cornet in which the player uses a mute to get a sort of wah-wah effect. When the singer comes back, she doesn't sing the words at the beginning of each phrase, but hums sustained notes in a way that is very moving. There's a very straightforward ending.

5  I've heard the band play this piece often on TV in recent years, so I think it must be their theme. But the version I'm talking about came from an old recording. It starts with a piano introduction, rather like the one the Ink Spots used to use, only faster. There are two choruses on piano then, in a very spare economical style. It's a twelve-bar blues, so the choruses are quite short. At the end of his second chorus, the piano player changes key abruptly. In the new key, the first solo is by tenor-saxophone, with a big breathy tone rather like Coleman Hawkins, though I know it isn't him. Then there's an ordinary sort of trombone solo followed by another tenor sax. At least, I *think* it's a tenor sax, although compared with the first one he has a much lighter sound, and in places it sounds as if it could be an alto. After a trumpet solo, there's a bit where the piano just plays plinky chords while the bass, guitar and drums keep the rhythm going. It ends with the band playing three choruses in which the trumpets, trombones and saxophones all play different phrases against each other. It's this part that the band played on TV.

# Twenty

## More Family Likenesses

Here are some more family likenesses, a trifle harder this time. As before, there are five pairs of blood relations. No clues this time, just pair them up. (One mark for each face you identify, an extra mark for completing the pair. Maximum, 15 marks)

1

2

3

4

5

6

7

8

9

10

# Twenty-one

## Praise from Fellow Musicians

The following are edited comments made by musicians – not all of them jazz musicians – about famous names in the jazz world. To whom are they referring? (One mark each. Maximum 5 marks)

1 'There is in the Southern Syncopated Orchestra an extraordinary clarinet virtuoso who is, so it seems, the first of his race to have composed perfectly formed blues on the clarinet . . . What a moving thing it is to meet this very black fat boy with white teeth and that narrow forehead, who is very glad one likes what he does, but who can say nothing of his art, save that he follows "his own way", and when one thinks that his "own way" is perhaps the highway the whole world will swing along tomorrow'.
*The Swiss conductor Ernest Ansermet, circa 1919*

2 'His style of improvisation would seem to have combined the highest reaches of instrumental virtuosity with the most tensely disciplined melodic structure and the most spontaneous emotional expression, all of which in one man you must admit to be pretty rare'.
*American composer Virgil Thompson, 1936*

3 'The real interest of --------'s records lies not so much in their colour, brilliant though it may be, as in the amazingly skilful proportions in which the colour is used. . . . He is definitely a petit maître, but that, after all, is considerably more than many people thought either jazz or the coloured race would ever produce. He has crystallised the popular music of our time and set up a standard by which we may judge not only other jazz composers but also those highbrow composers, whether American or English, who indulge in what is roughly known as "symphonic jazz"'.
*The British composer and conductor Constant Lambert, 1933*

**4** 'He gave up his position with the Denver Symphony to organize and lead a class jazz band. Despite his classical background, he didn't have a snooty bone in his body. Now there have been those who have come on the scene, grabbed the money, and run off to a plush life of boredom, but nobody held on to his band like ------ did. He was always adding interesting musicians to his payroll, without regard to their behaviour. All he wanted was to have those giant cats blow, and they blew up a storm'.
*Duke Ellington*

**5** 'His style of piano playing was something altogether new to me. It was full of old-time idioms; authentic old-fashioned ragtime; but scattered throughout the ragtime were occasionally incongruously modern modulatory passages – these last all his own, so far as I've ever been able to determine, for I have never heard anyone else play anything quite like them. . . . At that time he had achieved a certain celebrity in coloured musicians' circles; but it wasn't until quite a while later that the white musicians got to know about him'.
*Artie Shaw*

# Twenty-two

## Faces and Names

Here is another set of faces to which you have to put a name from the accompanying list. The only snag is that the list contains the real names of the artists, not those by which they are known. (One mark for identifying the face, and an extra mark for picking the right name. Maximum, 20 marks)

Richard Penniman

Frank Paul LoVecchio

Norma Egstrom

Paul Breitenfeld

Kenneth Norville

Peter Chatman

Theodore Leopold Friedman

Ian Ernest Gilmore Green

Kathryn Starks

Gertrude Melissa Nix Pridgett

1

2

3

4

5

6

7

8

9

10

# Twenty-three

## The Story Behind the Tune

Events and situations great and small have inspired jazz composers over the years. Below are listed some circumstances from which a tune or a title have emerged. Name the tune. (One mark each. Maximum 10 marks)

1 In 1909, during a mayoral campaign in Memphis, Tennessee, the bandleader and composer W.C. Handy was hired to write a campaign tune for one of the candidates. Mr E.H. Crump. After the campaign, the tune 'Mr Crump' was embellished with additional themes and published under a new title.

2 Duke Ellington was sharing a taxi with lyric writer Nick Kenny, who asked the Duke where he would like to be put down. Ellington's answer provided the title for one of his best-known tunes.

3 When Fats Waller was appearing at the Paramount Theatre, Los Angeles, he commented, in characteristically ribald style, on the ample rear view of singer Kitty Murray, who was on the same bill. Later, his personal remark was amplified into a lyric and immortalised in a Waller song.

4 Billy Strayhorn, Duke Ellington's friend and collaborator, was inspired by a famous Whistler painting to compose a tune – to which he then gave the wrong title! It was only when he came to London several years later that he visited the scene of Whistler's painting and discovered his mistake.

5 In 1938, the Chicagoan cornettist Muggsy Spanier was taken ill and spent several months in the Touro Infirmary, New Orleans.

6 Lulu White, the aunt of composer Spencer Williams, owned a celebrated 'sporting house' or bordello in the Storyville district of New Orleans. Her nephew immortalised it in a well-known stomp.

7 In 1776, Alexander Milne emigrated from England to America, settling in New Orleans, where he made his fortune. He bought land on the shores of Lake Ponchartrain and built a summer resort, which was named after him. The Jelly Roll Morton composition derived from this playground is chronically misspelt and mispronounced.

**8** At a street car junction in Birmingham, Alabama, workers from the railroads and steel mills used to change from their working clothes into evening wear prior to a night out on the tiles. History is vague as to whether they used a convenient wash-house or a store that hired out dress suits, but it is believed that the intersection took its name from the nightly occurrence. The tune named after it was a big Glenn Miller hit.

**9** George W. Johnson, a schoolteacher and amateur poet, wrote a love poem for his sweetheart, Maggie Clark. Their marriage in 1865 was short-lived, as she died a few months later. The poem, set to music by James Austin Butterfield, was a big hit in 1866, and has survived to provide an occasional theme for jazz musicians.

**10** The pianist James P. Johnson, playing in clubs around Harlem from 1912 onwards, had to cater to the demands of migrants from the area of Georgia and South Carolina who had flooded into the district. Inspired by their wild and eccentric dancing he wrote a show tune named after the city from which many of them came. In 1923 it became a hit and launched a worldwide dance craze.

# Twenty-four

## Tell-Tale Details

Below are details of photographs which should be enough to enable you to identify the musicians. (One mark each. Maximum 10 marks)

**1**

**2**

3

4

5

6

7

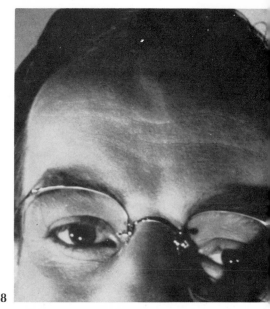

8

9

10

# Twenty-five

## Countries of Birth

Give the country of birth of the following musicians. (One mark each. Maximum 10 marks)

1 Ray Noble

2 Django Reinhardt

3 André Previn

4 Joe Venuti

5 Kai Winding

6 Art Hodes

7 George Chisholm

8 Guy Lombardo

9 Laurindo Almeida

10 Martial Solal

*Joe Venuti*

# Twenty-six

## Unflattering Remarks

Not all the comments by musicians upon their colleagues have been imbued with sweetness and light. See if you can identify the recipients of the following rude or unflattering remarks. (One mark each. Maximum, 10 marks)

1 Of whom did Ethel Waters remark that she sang as if her shoes were too tight?

2 Who prompted Duke Ellington to say 'He played piano like one of those high school teachers in Washington. As a matter of fact, high school teachers played better jazz.'?

3 Of which member of the 'cool school' of jazz did Eddie Condon exclaim that he sounded 'like a female alcoholic'?

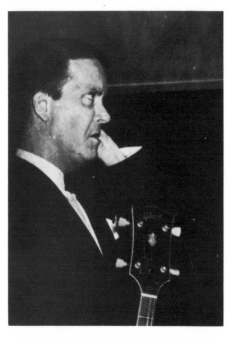

*Eddie Condon*

4 Which legendary jazz figure did Louis Armstrong sum up in this way. 'All in all, he was a great musician, but I think he blew too hard. I will even go so far as to say that he did not blow correctly. In any case he finally went crazy. You can figure that out for yourself.'?

5 Whom did Stan Kenton have in mind when he said 'If --- ------- can be credited with one thing, it is that they came along and they made fans out of six- and seven-year-old kids. They took it down that low. And the adults went for that stuff, because I think it's natural that an adult feels a kid is more perceptive and hip. And so they started looking at those things and started reading things into them. But there really wasn't anything there. It's just children's music.'

6 Who prompted this outburst from Jelly Roll Morton: '------ cannot prove anything in music that he has created. He has possibly taken advantage of some unprotected material that floats around . . . these untruthful statements that ---

has made, or caused you to make, will maybe cause him to be branded the most dastardly imposter in the history of music.'?

7 To which famous rival, according to Billie Holiday, did Lester Young once say, tapping his forehead 'There's things going on up there, man . . . some of you guys are all belly.'?

8 Of whom did Miles Davis complain 'He never gives any support to the rhythm section. When I had him on my date, I had him lay out until the ensemble. I like to hear him play, but I can't stand him in a rhythm section unless it's one of his own songs.'?

9 Of whom was Sidney Bechet talking when he said 'It seemed like he was wanting to make it a kind of thing where we were supposed to be bucking each other, competing instead of working together for that real feeling that would let the music come new and strong. And the funny thing is that I can remember ----- years ago when he was so timid you'd have to urge him to get up and play when there was some *regular* bucking kind of session going on. . . .'?

10 Who was Frank Walker, an executive of Columbia records in the early Twenties, describing when he recalled 'She looked anything *but* a singer. She looked about seventeen, tall and fat and scared to death – just awful'.

*Miles Davis*

# Twenty-seven

## Unusual Jazz Instruments

Here are some instruments which are in varying degrees unusual as jazz solo instruments. Identify them, and then answer the question attached to each. (One mark for a correct identification, an extra mark for answering the question. Maximum, 20 marks)

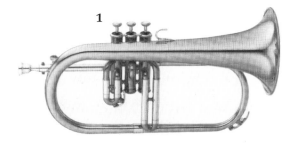

**1** Who successfully introduced this instrument into the Duke Ellington Orchestra in the 1950s?

**2** What has this instrument in common with the tenor sax, flute, argol, rebob and earth-board?

**3** Whose performance of 'Junk Man', with Jack Teagarden's Orchestra, brought this aristocrat on to the jazz scene?

**4** Who saw an instrument like this in the window of a London shop, bought it out of curiosity and went on to make his name on it?

5 In what famous band was this work-horse of the rhythm section first promoted to the front-line?

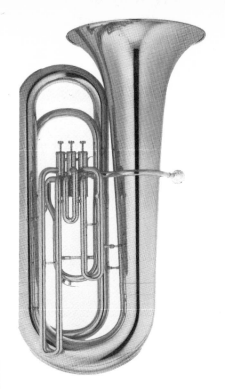

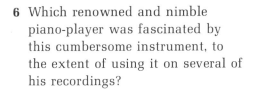

6 Which renowned and nimble piano-player was fascinated by this cumbersome instrument, to the extent of using it on several of his recordings?

7 Which musician, at times associated with the bands of Stan Kenton and Shorty Rogers and other West Coast groups, pioneered the use of this difficult instrument as a solo jazz voice?

8 Which heavyweight boogie-woogie exponent stretched incongruity to its limits by recording on this fragile instrument?

9 Who has the triple distinction of having played piano for Louis Armstrong, trumpet for Eddie Condon and this unusual instrument all over the place?

10 Which classically trained drummer introduced this instrument into recordings by Red Nichols in the Twenties?

# Twenty-eight

## True or False?

Here, as we near the end, is something to make a meal of – a wealth of information, much of which is untrue. All you have to do is decide which statement is true and which is false. (One mark each. Maximum 30 marks)

1 Cue Porter was a fine and underrated alto-saxophonist who played in a style similar to Johnny Hodges.

2 The evergreen dance favourite, 'Charleston', was written by the Harlem pianist James P. Johnson.

3 The New Orleans clarinettist Irving Fazola, born Prestopnik, took his professional name from the three notes of tonic sol-fa, FA-SOH-LA.

4 Sonny Rollins was born on the Caribbean island of St Thomas.

5 The veteran pianist Lucky Roberts was so-called because of his success as a gambler.

6 Benito Mussolini's son is a prominent jazz pianist in Italy.

7 Duke Ellington never used a tenor-saxophone in his band until Ben Webster joined him in the mid-Thirties.

8 Sidney Bechet was jailed for eleven months in Paris in 1928 for taking part in a shooting affray on the streets of Paris.

9 Pictured here is the renowned blues pianist, Cripple Clarence Lofton.

10 The famous singer Al Bowlly was killed in a car crash in California while touring America with Ray Noble's Band.

11 Spain has never produced a jazz musician of note.

12 Peggy Lee, whose real name is Norma Egstrom, was born in Sweden and travelled to America with her family when she was three years old.

13 The comedian Dudley Moore was at one time the pianist in Johnny Dankworth's Orchestra.

14 Turner Layton, singer, pianist and erstwhile member of the song team Layton and Johnston, was also a songwriter and took a part in writing such favourites as 'After You've Gone' and 'Way Down Yonder in New Orleans'.

15 The British jazz critic Benny Green was formerly a professional trombonist.

16 The great gospel-singer Mahalia Jackson, pictured below, was for a time vocalist with Duke Ellington's Orchestra.

**22** Louis Armstrong once played Bottom in a musical version of *A Midsummer Night's Dream*.

**23** Jelly Roll Morton named his composition 'Wolverine Blues' after the Wolverine Orchestra, the band in which Bix Beiderbecke played in 1924.

**24** The drummer and bandleader Ben Pollack committed suicide in 1971.

**25** The tenor-saxist Zoot Sims is pictured here with guitarist Joe Pass during a Jazz At The Philharmonic tour.

**17** Vibraphonist Milt Jackson, above, has recorded several solos on piano, using a rapid percussive style with the two forefingers striking the keys like mallets.

**18** The middle name of boogie-woogie pianist Meade Lux Lewis derived from a childhood nickname, 'The Duke of Luxembourg'.

**19** Coleman Hawkins recorded the first jazz version of the popular song 'Body and Soul' in 1939.

**20** The King of Thailand is a jazz enthusiast and plays the alto saxophone.

**21** Paul Gonsalves and Clark Terry have shared the experience of working in the bands of both Count Basie and Duke Ellington.

**26** Lil Hardin, below, the pianist with King Oliver's Creole Jazz Band, was Louis Armstrong's first wife and was thenceforward known as Lil Armstrong.

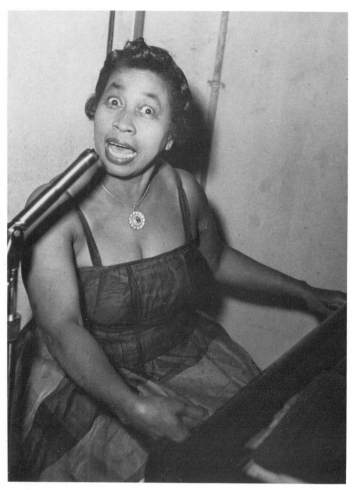

**27** The term 'Viper' was Harlem slang for someone addicted to narcotics, principally cocaine.

**28** Lester Young's earliest professional work in music was as a drummer.

**28** Leon 'Chu' Berry was given his nickname by fellow-musicians because of his alleged resemblance to the stage character Chu Chin Chow.

**30** Duke Ellington wrote 'In a Mellotone', a tune based on the harmonies of 'Rose Room'. A 'Mellotone' was a type of trombone mute.

# Twenty-nine

## Zoological Nicknames

Finally, to let the brain unwind, here are a few more nicknames with zoology as the common factor. Put one or two names to each one to identify the owner. (One mark each. Maximum 10 marks)

1 Bird

2 Hawk

3 Cat

4 Bunny

5 Rabbit

6 Cow Cow

7 Mousey

8 Pony

9 Mule

10 Honeybear

# Answers

**QUIZ ONE, page 9: Bandleaders and their Instruments**
  **1** Woody Herman, clarinet.
  **2** Duke Ellington, piano.
  **3** Buddy Rich, drums.
  **4** Ted Heath, trombone.
  **5** Lionel Hampton, vibraphone.
  **6** Gene Krupa, drums.
  **7** Harry James, trumpet.
  **8** Glenn Miller, trombone.
  **9** Stan Kenton, piano.
**10** Benny Goodman, clarinet.

**QUIZ TWO, page 13: Musicians' Titles**
  **1** W.C. Handy.
  **2** Big Joe Turner.
  **3** Lester Young.
  **4** Thelonious Monk.
  **5** Billie Holiday.
  **6** Jimmy Rushing.
  **7** Benny Goodman.
  **8** Tommy Dorsey.
  **9** Cab Calloway.
**10** Billie Eckstine.

**QUIZ THREE, page 14: Musicians and their Nicknames**
  **1** Williams.
  **2** Jay McShann.
  **3** Wood.
  **4** Albert Heath.
  **5** Singleton.
  **6** Cutshall.
  **7** Sims.
  **8** Mussulli.
  **9** Walter Thomas.
**10** Mondello or Camarata, and also
      Thielemans.

**QUIZ FOUR, page 15: Bands, Past and Present**

  **1** The World's Greatest Jazz Band.
  **2** The Dukes of Dixieland.
  **3** The Crusaders.
  **4** The Temperance Seven.
  **5** The Modern Jazz Quartet.
  **6** The Original Dixieland Jazz Band.
  **7** Weather Report.
  **8** The Quintet of the Hot Club of France.
  **9** The Jazz Messengers.
 **10** The Dutch Swing College Band.

**QUIZ FIVE, page 21: Dramatic Deaths**

  **1** Charlie Parker.
  **2** Fats Waller.
  **3** Glen Miller.
  **4** Bessie Smith.
  **5** Tommy Dorsey.
  **6** Clarence 'Pinetop' Smith.
  **7** Ken 'Snakehips' Johnson.
  **8** Frank Teschemacher.
  **9** Johnny Hodges.
 **10** Trombonist Charlie Green.

**QUIZ SIX, page 22: Singers and their Bands**

  **1** Peggy Lee, Benny Goodman.
  **2** Billy Eckstine, Earl Hines.
  **3** Anita O'Day, Gene Krupa.
  **4** Joe Williams, Count Basie.
  **5** Frank Sinatra, Tommy Dorsey.
  **6** Doris Day. Les Brown.
  **7** Ella Fitzgerald, Chick Webb.
  **8** Bing Crosby, Paul Whiteman.
  **9** Lena Horne, Charlie Barnet.
 **10** Sarah Vaughan, Earl Hines.

**QUIZ SEVEN, page 25: Tunes and their Composers**

  **1** Ray Bauduc and Bob Haggart.
  **2** Jelly Roll Morton.
  **3** Nancy Hamilton and Morgan Lewis.
  **4** Juan Tizol.
  **5** James P. Johnson.
  **6** Henry Creamer and Turner Layton.
  **7** Bobby Timmons.
  **8** Horace Silver.
  **9** Shelton Brooks.
 **10** Hughie Cannon.

1 C    1 W.C.H
2 P    3 LY
3 D    4
4 T/B   5 BH
5 ✓    6 JR
6 D    7 B.G.
7 T
8 T/B
9 P
10 C

...nd Django Reinhardt, of the Quintet of the Hot Club of

...on and Kai Winding, whose partnership was known as 'J & K'.
...al Desmond, associated for many years in the Dave Brubeck

...Stewart, a novelty jazz duo known as 'Slim and Slam'.
...vis, co-leaders of the 'Thad Jones–Mel Lewis Big Band'.

...rom New Orleans. He was born in Texarkana, Texas,
...ragtime centre of St Louis.
...Joplin was not related to the black composer Scott

...score for *The Sting*, a film that was shot decades after
...in 1917. 'The Entertainer', used by the film's composer, Marvin
Hamlisch, was copyrighted in 1902.

(d) *The Sting* starred Paul Newman and Robert Redford, not Peter Fonda and Redford.

(e) Scott Joplin did write a folk opera called *Treemonisha*, but the march 'Blaze Away' was written by Abe Holzmann, better known to jazz archivists for a cakewalk called 'Smoky Mokes'.

2 (a) Nick La Rocca played cornet, not piano.

(b) On 30 January 1917, the ODJB recorded 'Darktown Strutters Ball' and 'Indiana' for the Columbia Record Company. This coupling was their first recording, although it was not released at once. The first ODJB tunes to be released, on 7 March 1917, were 'Dixie Jazz Band One-Step' (later retitled 'Original Dixieland One-Step') and 'Livery Stable Blues'. The first version of 'Tiger Rag' was not recorded until August, 1917.

(c) Tommy Dorsey *did* record a version on trumpet, but in 1928. By 1935 he was known exclusively as a trombonist and the leader of the newly formed Tommy Dorsey Orchestra.

(d) Louis Armstrong made several recordings of 'Tiger Rag', but never with his Hot Five, the little band with which he recorded prolifically between 1925 and 1928. His first recording of the tune was made in 1930.

(e) The words 'Hold that Tiger!' do not appear in the ODJB's recording of 'Tiger Rag'. Indeed, they were added much later.

3 (a) In the Jones family, Thad Jones is the trumpeter, Elvin the drummer. (Give yourself one mark for each)

(b) Mamie Smith, Clara Smith, Trixie Smith and Bessie Smith, all renowned blues singers, were not related.

(c) Bessie Smith was dubbed 'The Empress of the Blues'.

(d) The Teagarden family came from Vernon, Texas.

(e) Jack Teagarden was one of the greatest jazz trombonists.

(f) Marian McPartland is not the sister of Jimmy and Dick. Born Marian Turner in Windsor, England, she married Jimmy McPartland in 1945.

4 (a) It was Joe Williams who recorded 'Ev'ry Day I Have the Blues' with Count Basie.

(b) Count Basie's first name is William, or Bill, not Bob.

(c) Peter Chatman is a fine blues singer, but he is known as Memphis Slim. Sunnyland Slim is also a blues singer, whose real name is Albert Luandrew.

(d) It is Neal, *not* Neil Hefti.

(e) Neal Hefti did not arrange 'Ev'ry Day', although from the Fifties onwards he has written many compositions and arrangements for Basie. The arranger of 'Ev'ry Day' was the former Basie tenor saxophonist, Frank Foster.

5 (a) Glenn Miller did not compose 'In the Mood', although he did the arrangement. The composer was Joe Garland, who had previously given the number to Artie Shaw. He could not record it because in its original form it ran longer than three minutes (the standard length of a 78 rpm record). It was Miller who trimmed and fashioned it into the enormously successful hit of 1939.

(b) 'In the Mood' was not the signature tune of Glenn Miller's Orchestra. That was 'Moonlight Serenade'. It was the English Joe Loss Orchestra that adopted 'In the Mood' as its introductory music.

(c) The familiar, repetitive twelve-bar theme of 'In the Mood' was not original to that piece. It certainly appears in 'Tar Paper Stomp', 'Jumpy Nerves' and 'Hot and Anxious', but they all came first.

(d) The Bobby Hackett cornet solo was not a feature of 'In the Mood' but of another Miller Hit, 'String of Pearls'.

(e) The Glenn Miller film biography was, of course, 'The Glenn Miller Story'. 'The Five Pennies' was the title of the film about bandleader and cornetist, Red Nichols.

(f) It is Syd Lawrence, not Elliot Lawrence (an American bandleader) who leads a British band specialising in the Miller sound.

(g) Acker Bilk does not specialise in Miller's music at all – his is a Dixieland or New Orleans style band.

(h) The distinctive Glenn Miller sound is a blend of a single clarinet, not trombone, with the saxophone section. It is the result of using the clarinet as the leading voice in place of the conventional alto saxophone, and of scoring in very close harmony.

## QUIZ TEN, page 32: Familiar Faces– Strange Names

1 Anthony Dominick Benedetto, otherwise Tony Bennett.

2 Ruth Jones, otherwise Dinah Washington.

3 Ferdinand Joseph La Menthe, otherwise Jelly Roll Morton.

4 Annabelle Short, otherwise Annie Ross.

5 Lester Polfus, otherwise Les Paul.

6 Eleanora McKay, otherwise Billie Holiday.

7 McKinley Morganfield, otherwise blues singer Muddy Waters.

8 Clive Powell, otherwise Georgie Fame.

9 Arthur Arshawsky, otherwise Artie Shaw.

10 Salvatore Massaro, otherwise guitarist Eddie Lang.

**QUIZ ELEVEN, page 36: Books and Authors**

    **1** Charles Mingus.

    **2** Billie Holiday.

    **3** Artie Shaw.

    **4** George Melly.

    **5** Duke Ellington.

    **6** Eddie Condon.

    **7** Humphrey Lyttelton.

    **8** Sidney Bechet.

    **9** Willie 'The Lion' Smith.

    **10** Mezz Mezzrow.

**QUIZ TWELVE, page 37: Family Likenesses**

Pictures 1 and 5 are of trombonist Jack Teagarden and his brother, trumpeter Charlie Teagarden.

2 and 7 are of two singers, Nat King Cole and his daughter Natalie Cole.

3 and 10 are of the New Orleans clarinettist Johnny Dodds and his brother, drummer Warren 'Baby' Dodds.

4 and 8 are of bandleader Duke Ellington and his son Mercer Ellington, also a bandleader.

6 and 9 are of Bing Crosby and his brother, bandleader Bob Crosby.

**QUIZ THIRTEEN, page 41: A Mixed Bag**

    **1** Harry James.

    **2** British pianist and composer Stan Tracey.

    **3** Seventy-one. He died on 6 July 1971.

    **4** W.C. Handy.

    **5** Woody Herman – the piece was called 'Ebony Concerto'.

    **6** John Dankworth.

    **7** Benny Goodman.

    **8** They are all Canadian by birth.

    **9** In 1938, when it was recorded by Louis Armstrong's Band.

    **10** Jimmy 'Schnozzle' Durante.

    **11** Spencer Williams.

    **12** Andy Razaf, who wrote the lyrics for most of Fats Waller's tunes.

    **13** Louis Armstrong to King George V, when the latter attended an Armstrong concert in London in the early Thirties.

    **14** Assuming that both are the standard B flat model, the length of tubing is the same. It differs in bore and the way it is assembled.

    **15** Eubie Blake.

    **16** Artie Shaw.

    **17** A short musical phrase or figure, repeated over and over again.

    **18** Joe 'King' Oliver.

    **19** Louis Armstrong's 1930 recording ot 'Memories of You'.

    **20** They were the four members of the singing group, the Hi-Los.

    **21** The pianist Willie 'The Lion' Smith.

    **22** Brass. It roughly resembles a French Horn.

    **23** Duke Ellington's 'A Drum is a Woman', a television work involving song, dance and commentary.

24 Joe Marsala.
25 Guitarist Eddie Lang, who occasionally used the pseudonym.
26 The John Kirby Sextet.
27 A French jazz enthusiast and critic, he wrote *Hot Discographie*, the first attempt at a complete jazz discography.
28 The band-boy and factotum to Duke Ellington's band in the Thirties, after whom Duke wrote the tune 'Stompy Jones'.
29 'The Waiter and the Porter and the Upstairs Maid' – a song which all three sang in the 1941 film 'Birth of the Blues'.
30 Ralph Burns. It was recorded by Woody Herman's Band.
31 Fats Waller. The show included 'Ain't Misbehavin' and 'Black and Blue', and featured Louis Armstrong as a soloist.
32 An instrument invented by the trombonist Brad Gowans that combined the characteristics of a valve and slide trombone.
33 1959.
34 Jelly Roll Morton.
35 Bud Powell. The other three pianists were, or are, all blind.
36 Guy Lombardo and his Royal Canadians.
37 Charles Mingus.
38 Count Basie, whose band recorded a tune of that name. He was born in Red Bank, New Jersey.
39 They are all trumpet mutes.
40 Take a mark for either Wingie Manone or Ken Colyer.
41 Jazz at the Philharmonic.
42 Paul Whiteman.
43 Sidney Bechet.
44 John Lewis, Milt Jackson, Percy Heath and Kenny Clarke.
45 Blues-singer Leroy Carr.
46 A famous ballroom in Harlem.
47 Bix Beiderbecke.
48 Sonny Rollins.
49 An instrument looking like a saxophone but equipped with metal reeds like a harmonica, whose sound it approximated.
50 All were once married to Ava Gardner.

**QUIZ FOURTEEN, page 43: Nicknames and Real Names**
1 John Birks Gillespie.
2 Charles Ellsworth Russell.
3 Leon Beiderbecke.
4 William Basie.
5 Antoine Domino.
6 Wilbur Clayton.
7 Julian Adderley.
8 Charles Melvin Williams.
9 Bernard Bilk.
10 Francis Spanier.

**QUIZ FIFTEEN, page 47: Biographies**

     **1** Charlie Christian.
     **2** Bunk Johnson.
     **3** Erroll Garner.
     **4** John Hammond.
     **5** Ronnie Scott.
     **6** Earl Bostic.
     **7** Victor Feldman.
     **8** Louis Prima.
     **9** Dave Brubeck.
     **10** Freddie Keppard.

**QUIZ SIXTEEN, page 49: Married Couples**

     **1** Chris Barber and Ottilie Patterson.
     **2** Mildred Bailey and Red Norvo.
     **3** John Dankworth and Cleo Laine.
     **4** Louis Bellson and Pearl Bailey.
     **5** Jimmy and Marian McPartland.

**QUIZ SEVENTEEN, page 52: 'Scrambled' Bands**

     **1** Fats Waller and his Rhythm.
     **2** Les Brown and his Band of Renown.
     **3** Nat Gonella's Georgians.
     **4** Louis Jordan's Tympani Five.
     **5** Guy Lombardo's Royal Canadians.
     **6** Jelly Roll Morton's Red Hot Peppers.
     **7** Louis Armstrong and his Hot Five.'
     **8** Andy Kirk and his Clouds of Joy.
     **9** King Oliver's Creole Jazz Band.
     **10** Red Nichols and his Five Pennies.

**QUIZ EIGHTEEN, page 53: Vocal Groups**

     **1** The Mills Brothers.
     **2** Lambert, Hendricks and Ross.
     **3** The Andrews Sisters.
     **4** The Rhythm Boys.
     **5** The Ink Spots.
     **6** The Pied Pipers.
     **7** The Boswell Sisters.
     **8** The Swingle Singers.
     **9** The Hi-Los.
     **10** The Deep River Boys.

**QUIZ NINETEEN, page 57: Descriptions of Recordings**

    **1** 'West End Blues' by Louis Armstrong's Band in 1928. The pianist was Earl Hines.

    **2** 'Sing, Sing, Sing' by Benny Goodman's Orchestra in 1937, with Gene Krupa on drums. The 'slightly familiar' second theme is the swing number, 'Christopher Columbus', transposed into a minor key and incorporated into the arrangement.

    **3** 'Potato Head Blues' by Louis Armstrong's Hot Seven in 1927. The clarinettist was Johnny Dodds.

    **4** 'Nobody Knows You When You're Down and Out' by Bessie Smith with accompaniment directed by Clarence Williams.

    **5** 'One O'Clock Jump' by Count Basie's Band in 1937. The first tenor saxophone was Herschel Evans, the second, Lester Young.

**QUIZ TWENTY, page 59: More Family Likenesses**

    Pictures 1 and 6 are of two brothers, bandleaders Tommy and Jimmy Dorsey.

    2 and 7 are of father and son, Boogie Woogie pianist Albert Ammons and tenor saxist Gene Ammons.

    3 and 8 are of two brothers, Nat and Cannonball Adderley.

    4 and 9 are of father and son, singers Alan and Jack Jones.

    5 and 10 are of two bandleading brothers, Fletcher and Horace Henderson.

**QUIZ TWENTY-ONE, page 62: Praise from Fellow Musicians**

    **1** Sidney Bechet.

    **2** Louis Armstrong.

    **3** Duke Ellington.

    **4** Paul Whiteman.

    **5** Willie 'The Lion' Smith.

**QUIZ TWENTY-TWO, page 64: Faces and Names**

    **1** Kenneth Norville, otherwise Red Norvo.

    **2** Kathryn Starks, otherwise Kay Starr.

    **3** Paul Breitenfeld, otherwise Paul Desmond.

    **4** Gertrude Melissa Nix Pridgett, otherwise Ma Rainey.

    **5** Ian Ernest Gilmore Green, otherwise Gil Evans.

    **6** Richard Penniman, otherwise Little Richard.

    **7** Frank Paul LoVecchio, otherwise Frankie Laine.

    **8** Peter Chatman, otherwise Memphis Slim.

    **9** Norma Egstrom, otherwise Peggy Lee.

    **10** Theodore Leopold Friedman, otherwise bandleader Ted Lewis.

**QUIZ TWENTY-THREE, page 68: The Story Behind the Tune**

    1 'Memphis Blues'.
    2 'Drop Me Off At Harlem'.
    3 'All That Meat And No Potatoes'.
    4 'Chelsea Bridge'.
    5 'Relaxin' At The Touro'.
    6 'Mahogany Hall Stomp'.
    7 'Milenberg Joys'.
    8 'Tuxedo Junction'.
    9 'When You And I Were Young, Maggie'.
   10 'Charleston'.

**QUIZ TWENTY-FOUR, page 70, Tell-Tale Details**

    1 The familiar white handkerchief of Louis Armstrong.
    2 The uptilted trumpet which was specially designed for himself by Dizzy Gillespie.
    3 The waistcoat which, together with bowler hat, forms the band uniform of Mr Acker Bilk.
    4 Three saxophones in the mouth of multi-instrumentalist Rahsaan Roland Kirk.
    5 The white gardenia, made much of in the film *Lady sings the Blues*, that Billie Holiday wore in her hair.
    6 The top hat of bandleader Ted Lewis.
    7 The kid-gloved false hand of the one-armed trumpeter, Wingie Manone.
    8 The bespectacled eyes of Glenn Miller.
    9 The grin of drummer Gene Krupa.
   10 The strikingly individual, slanted-saxophone stance of Lester Young.

**QUIZ TWENTY-FIVE, page 73: Countries of Birth**

    1 England.
    2 Belgium.
    3 Germany.
    4 No country – he was born on board ship between Italy and the USA.
    5 Denmark.
    6 Russia.
    7 Scotland.
    8 Canada.
    9 Brazil.
   10 Algeria.

**QUIZ TWENTY-SIX, page 74: Unflattering Remarks**

  **1** Billie Holiday.
  **2** Jelly Roll Morton.
  **3** Paul Desmond.
  **4** Buddy Bolden.
  **5** The Beatles.
  **6** W.C. Handy.
  **7** Herschel Evans.
  **8** Thelonious Monk.
  **9** Louis Armstrong.
  **10** Bessie Smith.

**QUIZ TWENTY-SEVEN, page 76: Unusual Jazz Instruments**

  **1** Fluegelhorn, Clark Terry.
  **2** Oboe. It is part of the musical armoury of Yusef Lateef.
  **3** Harp, Caspar Reardon.
  **4** Straight soprano saxophone, Sidney Bechet.
  **5** Tuba, Miles Davis's nine-piece band of 1948/9, in which the player was Bill Barber.
  **6** Pipe organ, Fats Waller.
  **7** French horn, Johnny Graas.
  **8** Celeste, Meade Lux Lewis.
  **9** Alto horn, Dick Cary.
  **10** Timpano or kettledrum, usually used in combinations of two or more and thus better known in the plural, timpani. Vic Berton.

**QUIZ TWENTY-EIGHT, page 79: True or False?**

  **1** False – Cue Porter *was* Johnny Hodges, who often used his wife's name as a pseudonym.
  **2** True.
  **3** True.
  **4** False – he was born in New York City.
  **5** False – he was called Luckey, a shortening of the given name Luckeyeth.
  **6** True.
  **7** False – the clarinettist Barney Bigard sometimes doubled on tenor-sax, although Ben Webster was the first featured soloist on the instrument in Ellington's band.
  **8** True.
  **9** False – the picture is of blues-pianist Jimmy Yancey.
  **10** False – Al Bowlly was killed in a London air-raid in 1941.
  **11** False – the fine pianist Tete Montoliu is from Barcelona.
  **12** False – Peggy Lee, née Norma Egstrom, was born in Jamestown, North Dakota.
  **13** True.